NATIONAL GEOGRAPHIC KiDS

PUZZLE BOOK

HORSES
AND
PONIES

Published by Collins
An imprint of HarperCollins Publishers
Westerhill Road
Bishopbriggs
Glasgow G64 2QT
www.harpercollins.co.uk

HarperCollins Publishers
1st Floor, Watermarque Building, Ringsend Road, Dublin 4, Ireland

In association with National Geographic Partners, LLC

NATIONAL GEOGRAPHIC and the Yellow Border Design are trademarks of the National Geographic Society, used under license.

First published 2019

ISBN 978-0-00-832152-9

10 9 8 7 6 5

Printed in Glasgow by Bell & Bain Ltd.

If you would like to comment on any aspect of this book,
please contact us at the above address or online.
natgeokidsbooks.co.uk
collins.reference@harpercollins.co.uk

Paper from responsible sources.

Acknowledgements

Cover images
Front – white pony © Eric Isselee/Shutterstock.com; horseshoe © Polonska Polina/Shutterstock.com; black horse © Kwadrat/Shutterstock.com; funny horse © canadastock/ Shutterstock.com; white horse © mariait/Shutterstock.com

Back – white pony © Grigorita Ko/Shutterstock.com; carousel © Delpixel/Shutterstock.com; rocking horse © JasminkaM/Shutterstock.com; jumping horse © Irina Maksimova/Shutterstock.com

Images in order of appearance
P2 © picsbyst/Shutterstock.com; P3 © Abramova Kseniya/Shutterstock.com; P4 (t) © Callipso/Shutterstock.com; P4 (m) © Abramova Kseniya/Shutterstock.com; P4 (b) © Tana Lee Alves/Shutterstock.com; P5 (t) © Edoma/Shutterstock.com; P5 (m) © Warpaint/Shutterstock.com; P5 (b) © val lawless/Shutterstock.com; P7 © Olga_i/Shutterstock.com; P8 © mariait /Shutterstock.com; P9 © Eric Isselee/Shutterstock.com; P10 © Alla Berlezova/Shutterstock.com; P11 © Anke van Wyk/Shutterstock.com; P12 © Eric Isselee/Shutterstock.com; P13 © Abramova Kseniya/Shutterstock.com; P15 (tl) © Volker Rauch/Shutterstock.com; P15 (tr) © Vera Zinkova/Shutterstock.com; P15 (ml) © Iuliia Khabibullina/Shutterstock.com; P15 (mr) © Eric Isselee/Shutterstock.com; P15 (bl) © OlesyaNickolaeva/Shutterstock.com; P15 (br) © Callipso/Shutterstock.com; P16 © Eric Isselee/Shutterstock.com; P17 (t) © Eric Isselee/Shutterstock.com; P17 (b) © picsbyst/Shutterstock.com; P18 © Anastasija Popova/Shutterstock.com; P19 © Eric Isselee/Shutterstock.com; P21 © Grigorita Ko/Shutterstock.com; P22 © tony mills/Shutterstock.com; P23 © Bosnian/Shutterstock.com; P24 © Abramova Kseniya/Shutterstock.com; P25 © Linda Macpherson/Shutterstock.com; P26 © Eric Isselee/Shutterstock.com; P27 © Michael Steden/Shutterstock.com; P29 (tl) © Nicole Ciscato/Shutterstock.com; P29 (tr) © eastern light photography/Shutterstock.com; P29 (ml) © Nicole Ciscato/Shutterstock.com; P29 (mr) © Emi/Shutterstock.com; P29 (bl) © Dave Green/Shutterstock.com; P29 (br) © Steven Cole/Shutterstock.com; P30–31 © Peter Turner Photography/Shutterstock.com; P32 © mariait/Shutterstock.com; P33 © Steven Cole/Shutterstock.com; P34 © ducu59us/Shutterstock.com; P35 © Liza Myalovskaya/Shutterstock.com; P37 © dikkens/Shutterstock.com; P38 © Birute Vijeikiene/Shutterstock.com; P39 © Melory/Shutterstock.com; P40 © stockphoto mania/Shutterstock.com; P41 © Olga_i/Shutterstock.com; P42 © Angela Cini/Shutterstock.com; P43 © Eric Isselee/Shutterstock.com; P44–45 © colin13362/Shutterstock.com; P46 © Abramova Kseniya/Shutterstock.com; P47 © Tana Lee Alves/Shutterstock.com; P48 © Olga_i/Shutterstock.com; P49 © Abramova Kseniya/Shutterstock.com; P51 © Fabrice Jolivet/Shutterstock.com; P52 © anakondasp/Shutterstock.com; P53 © Alexey Wraith/Shutterstock.com; P54 © cynoclub/Shutterstock.com; P55 © GoodMood Photo/Shutterstock.com; P56 © VitaminCo/Shutterstock.com; P57 © UVgreen/Shutterstock.com; P59 (tl) © Melory/Shutterstock.com; P59 (tr) © Ramon grosso dolarea/Shutterstock.com; P59 (ml) © tetiana_u/Shutterstock.com; P59 (mr) © Jeffrey B. Banke/Shutterstock.com; P59 (bl) © Edoma/Shutterstock.com; P59 (br) © Josep Curto/Shutterstock.com; P60 © Nattika/Shutterstock.com; P61 © Roman Samokhin/Shutterstock.com; P62 © Smit/Shutterstock.com; P63 (t) © Lightspring/Shutterstock.com; P63 (b) © OlenaBykova/Shutterstock.com; P65 © Valentyna Chukhlyebova/Shutterstock.com; P66 © Warpaint/Shutterstock.com; P67 © Digital Storm/Shutterstock.com; P68 © Antracit/Shutterstock.com; P69 By Nicor - Own work, CC BY-SA 3.0, https://commons.wikimedia.org/w/index.php?curid=21296449; P70 © Sanit Fuangnakhon/Shutterstock.com; P71 © Zwiebackesser/Shutterstock.com; P72–73 © VeronArt16/Shutterstock.com; P74 © Rachael Arnott/Shutterstock.com; P75 © Joyce Nelson/Shutterstock.com; P76 © Cholpan/Shutterstock.com; P77 By Rosemania - https://www.flickr.com/photos/rosemania/4121249698, CC BY 2.0, https://commons.wikimedia.org/w/index.php?curid=9404223; P79 © val lawless/Shutterstock.com; P80 © bumihills/Shutterstock.com; P81 © Nicolas Economou/Shutterstock.com; P82 © DE ROCKER/Alamy Stock Photo; P83 © The Picture Art Collection/Alamy Stock Photo; P84 © Peter Hermes Furian/Shutterstock.com; P85 © STEVEN CHIANG/Shutterstock.com; P86–87 © Annette Shaff/Shutterstock.com; P88 © Chronicle/Alamy Stock Photo; P89 © Historic Collection/Alamy Stock Photo;

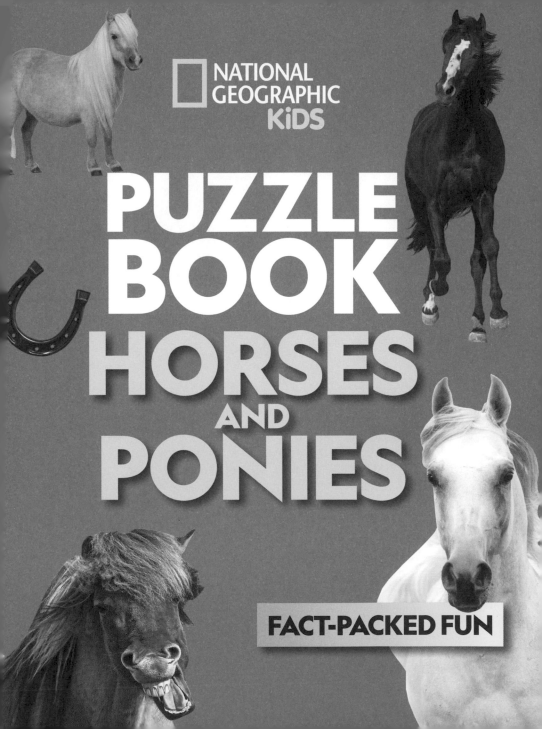

NATIONAL
GEOGRAPHIC
KiDS

PUZZLE BOOK
HORSES
AND
PONIES

FACT-PACKED FUN

CONTENTS

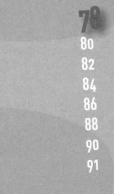

Happy horses

Saddle up for fun facts and puzzles on happy horses!

ANDALUSIAN HORSES are used a lot in **FILMS** due to their **LOOKS AND ENERGY.**

CROSSWORDS

Help the Arabian horse crack the crosswords by solving the cryptic clues below.
Answers have the same amount of letters as the number in brackets.
Can you work out the horse keyword using the letters in the shaded squares?
See if you are right by flicking to page 92.

The **ARABIAN HORSE** is over **5,000 YEARS** old and is known as the oldest and FIRST-DOMESTICATED breed of horse.

Across

1 Unable to be seen (9)
5 Baked dish in a pastry case (3)
7 Speak very quietly (7)
8 In the direction of (7)
11 Half of two (3)
12 Not permanent (9)

Down

1 Of great significance (9)
2 Outlook; field of vision (4)
3 Knock into (4)
4 Very (9)
6 People who do not tell the truth (5)
9 Quite hot (4)
10 Furniture item you sit on (4)

FRIESIAN HORSES are known for their beautiful LONG MANES and pure black colouring.

Across

1 Lower and raise your head as a way of saying yes (3)
5 Picture something in your mind (7)
7 Oxygen, for instance (3)
8 Time when farmers gather crops (7)
9 Say something in passing (7)
11 How old you are (3)
12 Admiration for someone (7)
13 Organ you see with (3)

Down

1 Very scary dream (9)
2 Not telling the truth (9)
3 Go to sleep through the winter (9)
4 Small creature with many legs (9)
6 Mixture of gases we breathe (3)
10 Frozen form of water (3)

SUDOKUS

Solve the sudokus with the American Quarter horse.
Fill in the blank squares so that numbers 1 to 6 appear once in each row,
column and 3 x 2 box. See if you are right by flicking to page 92.

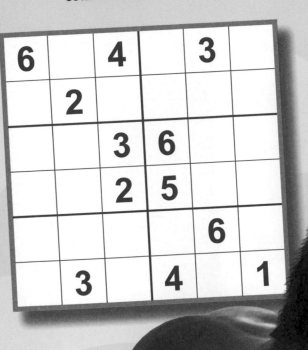

6		4		3	
	2				
		3	6		
		2	5		
				6	
	3		4		1

The **AMERICAN QUARTER** horse
can run a quarter of a mile
**(402 metres) IN
21 SECONDS!**

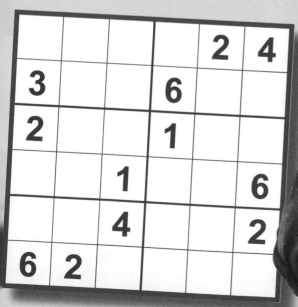

Wordsearches

The Appaloosa is on the lookout for its friends. Search left to right, up and down to find the words listed in the boxes below. See if you are right by flicking to page 92.

APPALOOSA HORSES have **SPOTTED COATS,** and some have **STRIPED HOOVES!**

h	m	u	s	t	a	n	g	l	o
o	a	a	y	c	s	t	y	f	u
r	i	f	t	o	t	r	r	r	j
s	i	c	e	l	a	n	d	i	c
e	q	a	t	t	l	t	a	e	v
e	a	p	p	a	l	o	o	s	a
y	g	e	l	d	i	n	g	i	p
e	i	r	k	d	o	f	o	a	l
s	e	q	u	i	n	e	x	n	p
m	n	d	s	g	e	a	r	u	

appaloosa	gelding
colt	horse eyes
equine	icelandic
foal	mustang
friesian	stallion

12

a	n	d	a	l	u	s	i	a	n
p	g	p	p	g	b	o	i	n	r
x	f	e	m	a	r	e	w	f	a
t	d	r	m	l	t	d	a	i	n
x	l	c	a	l	r	l	w	l	e
n	t	h	n	o	t	e	d	l	x
s	l	e	e	p	i	n	g	y	s
e	a	r	a	b	i	a	n	n	o
r	t	o	l	f	e	t	a	n	o
h	a	n	o	v	e	r	i	a	n

andalusian
arabian
filly
gallop
hanoverian

mane
mare
percheron
sleeping
tolfetano

The name **MUSTANG** comes from the **SPANISH-AMERICAN** word **"MESTENGO"**, meaning **"RANGING FREELY"**.

13

CLOSE UP

Match the mind-boggling magnifications to the named pictures opposite. See if you are right by flicking to page 93.

1

2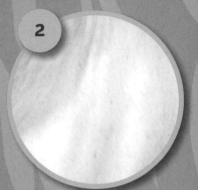

3

4

5

6

Norwegian Fjord horse

1

American Paint horse

2

Icelandic horse

3

Percheron

4

Friesian

5

Arabian

6

MAZES

Lead the Dutch warmblood through the maze. Work your way around the maze until you reach the exit. See if you are right by flicking to page 93.

HORSES are measured in hands that EQUAL 4 INCHES. DUTCH WARMBLOODS stand more than 15.2 HANDS HIGH (HH).

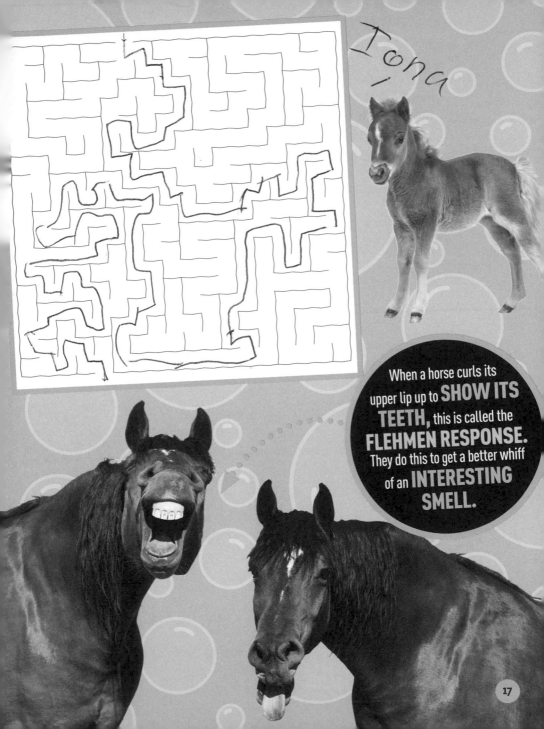

Iona

When a horse curls its upper lip up to **SHOW ITS TEETH,** this is called the **FLEHMEN RESPONSE.** They do this to get a better whiff of an **INTERESTING SMELL.**

GUESS WHAT?

Can you guess the answers to the horse questions below?
Check your guesses by flicking to page 93.

1. We measure the height of horses in:
   a) Feet ✓
   b) Hands ✓
   c) Arms

2. Which is the oldest breed of horse?
   a) Arabian
   b) Friesian
   c) Icelandic ✓

3. A baby horse under 1 year old is called a:
   a) Pup ✓
   b) Calf
   c) Foal

4. How many bones does a horse have?
   a) 205 ✓
   b) 255
   c) 175

5. Horses have bigger what than any other land mammals?
   a) Brain
   b) Tail
   c) Eyes ✓

6. All Appaloosa horses coats are:
   a) Dun ✓
   b) Spotted
   c) Striped

7. Percheron horses can reach the height of:
   a) 15 hands
   b) 17 hands ✓
   c) 19 hands

8. American quarter horses can run a quarter of a mile in:
   a) 21 seconds ✓
   b) 42 seconds ✓
   c) 60 seconds

9. Horses cannot:
   a) Snore
   b) Vomit ✓
   c) Lie down

10. No two horses of this breed have the same markings:
    a) American Paint horse
    b) British Clay horse
    c) Chinese Chalk horse

YOUNG MALE HORSES, usually below the age of four, are called **COLTS.** A filly is a female horse that is too young to be called a **MARE.**

WORD JUMBLES

Rearrange the jumbled letters to form horse-related words.
See if you are right by flicking to page 93.

L F Y I L

R N E O H C E P R

G M U T A S N

I N A R B A A

R A O E H N N V I A

HORSES
can sleep
both **LYING
DOWN** and
**STANDING
UP!**

Precious ponies

Explore this chapter for fun facts and puzzles about ponies.

SHETLAND PONIES were once used to work in **UNDERGROUND MINES.**

CROSSWORDS

Help the Exmoor pony crack the crosswords by solving the cryptic clues below.
Answers have the same amount of letters as the number in brackets.
Can you work out the pony keyword using the letters in the shaded squares?
See if you are right by flicking to page 94.

The **EXMOOR PONY** has lived on **EXMOOR, ENGLAND,** since ancient times and is one of Britain's **OLDEST PONY BREEDS.**

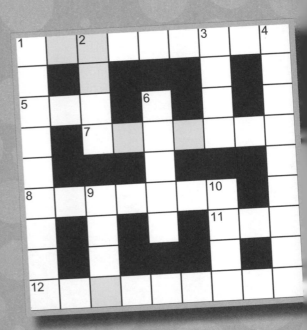

Across

1   Not allowed (9)
5   Sleep during the day (3)
7   Illustration; typical case (7)
8   Very important (7)
11   Small green vegetable (3)
12   A science (9)

Down

1   Impressive or incredible (9)
2   Strong cord (4)
3   Slightly wet (4)
4   Obligatory or required (9)
6   Christmas song (5)
9   Ready to eat (of fruit) (4)
10   Small dot (4)

The **DARTMOOR** pony is a native **BRITISH** breed. The **WILD PONIES** are rounded up by their owners during the annual **"DRIFT"** each **AUTUMN.**

Across

1 Far away (7)
6 Make free from dirt (5)
7 Animal that eats meat (9)
8 Picture (5)
9 Not artificial (7)

Down

1 One ___ : boy band (9)
2 Building designer (9)
3 Winnie-___-___ : A.A. Milne character (3-4)
4 Marvellous; great (9)
5 Sure (7)

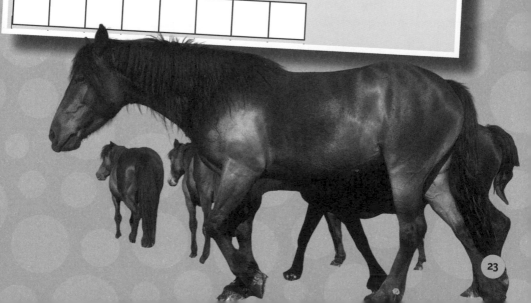

SUDOKUS

Solve the sudokus with the Welsh pony. Fill in the blank squares so that numbers 1 to 6 appear once in each row, column and 3 x 2 box. See if you are right by flicking to page 94.

				3	
	5		6		
3	4		1		
		2		6	3
		4		1	
	2				

WELSH PONIES used to help people **DELIVER THE POST.**

The **HIGHLAND PONY** is quite a rare breed, with approximately **5,500 IN THE WORLD TODAY.**

2			1	4	5
		5	2		
		1	5		
3	5	2			6

4	5				
1		3			
				1	2
2	6				
			1		3
				2	6

Wordsearches

The Haflinger is on the lookout for its friends. Search left to right, up and down to find the words listed in the boxes below. See if you are right by flicking to page 94.

w	e	l	s	h	j	h	o	o	f
a	s	s	a	t	e	a	g	u	e
k	q	a	n	u	a	f	r	k	p
e	w	m	d	z	s	l	e	e	g
r	i	q	a	t	t	i	x	r	r
i	t	n	l	r	u	n	m	r	p
s	h	y	w	t	r	g	o	y	k
k	e	g	o	n	c	e	o	b	p
a	r	a	o	r	o	r	r	o	p
y	s	o	d	f	n	b	h	g	o

assateague

asturcon

eriskay

exmoor

haflinger

hoof

kerry bog

sandalwood

welsh

withers

All **HAFLINGER PONIES** are a shade of chestnut, with a **PALE MANE AND TAIL.**

```
c o n n e m a r a s
b o s n i a n h s n
g k k a m r d i h e
o m r j v k a g e w
t r o t e i r h t f
l u s z f n t l l o
a k j b p g m a a r
n o y j u s o n n e
d u l m e n o d d s
k s i n u v r v k t
```

bosnian
connemara
dartmoor
dülmen
gotland

highland
markings
new forest
shetland
trot

CONNEMARA PONIES are good natured with a **GENTLE** and trusting temperament. This makes them perfect for **CHILDREN'S TREKKING.**

CLOSE UP

Match the mind-boggling magnifications to the named pictures opposite. See if you are right by flicking to page 95.

1

2

3

4

5

6
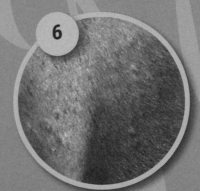

American Shetland pony

1

New Forest pony

2

Fell pony

3

Eriskay pony

4

Dales pony

5

Chincoteague pony

6

SPOT THE DIFFERENCE

Compare the two images of Dartmoor ponies.
Can you spot the five differences between the images?
See if you are right by flicking to page 95.

DARTMOOR PONIES are very hardy and actually thrive in **DARTMOOR NATIONAL PARK, ENGLAND,** despite the harsh weather and **POOR VEGETATION.**

MAZES

Lead the Welsh mountain pony through the maze. Work your way around the maze until you reach the exit. See if you are right by flicking to page 95.

WELSH MOUNTAIN PONIES are up to **12 HANDS HIGH,** and weigh about **225 KG.**

CHINCOTEAGUE PONIES are wild ponies that live in MARYLAND and VIRGINIA, USA. The herd may have been around for more than 500 YEARS!

GUESS WHAT?

Can you guess the answers to the pony questions below?
Check your guesses by flicking to page 95.

1. Ponies' manes are what compared to horses?
   a) Thicker
   b) Shorter
   c) More colourful

2. Shetland ponies can be any colour apart from:
   a) Chestnut
   b) Spotted
   c) Grey

3. Ponies' feet are called:
   a) Claws
   b) Fins
   c) Hooves

4. Haflinger ponies are what colour?
   a) Grey
   b) Black
   c) Chestnut

5. This pony is native to Germany:
   a) Dülmen
   b) Eriskay
   c) Shetland

6. Chincoteague ponies are good:
   a) Dancers
   b) Swimmers
   c) Painters

7. How high are Dales ponies?
   a) 10–11 hands
   b) 14–14.2 hands
   c) 11–12 hands

8. Bosnian ponies make up what percentage of the horse and pony population of Bosnia and Herzegovina?
   a) 70%
   b) 50%
   c) 100%

9. Patches of white hair on ponies' faces or legs are called:
   a) Tattoos
   b) Highlights
   c) Markings

10. Ponies are the perfect size for who to ride them?
   a) Adults
   b) Children
   c) Dogs

For their size, SHETLAND PONIES are the STRONGEST of all HORSES AND PONIES!

WORD JUMBLES

The Dülmen needs help to rearrange the jumbled letters to form pony-related words. See if you are right by flicking to page 95.

N M D L Ü E

O X O M R E

O R T D A M R O

E Y K I S R A

G U A E A S T S A E

The **DÜLMEN** is the only native pony in **GERMANY.** It has been around **SINCE THE 1300S.**

Work and play

Giddy up! Fun facts and puzzles on the world of horses are on the way.

Some horses are used for **RACING.** These horses are ridden by **JOCKEYS** at speeds of up to **43 MPH (69 KMH).**

CROSSWORDS

Help the police horse crack the crosswords by solving the cryptic clues below.
Answers have the same amount of letters as the number in brackets.
Can you work out the keyword using the letters in the shaded squares?
See if you are right by flicking to page 96.

Across

1 Easy to see or understand (7)
5 Put into service (3)
6 Small rodent kept as a pet (7)
8 Type of dance (5)
9 In place of something else (7)
11 Male child (3)
12 Force that pulls things towards earth (7)

Down

1 Else (9)
2 Opposite of in (3)
3 Outside part of something (7)
4 The day before today (9)
7 Early part of the day (7)
10 Mediterranean ___ : large body of water (3)

POLICE HORSES are trained to deal with **LARGE CROWDS** and **LOUD NOISES.**

Across

1. Where you go to get on an aeroplane (7)
5. Sprint (3)
6. Large African ape (7)
8. Game such as cricket or tennis (5)
9. Notice or perceive (7)
11. Member of a religious community of women (3)
12. Person who looks after teeth (7)

Down

1. Country in South America (9)
2. Liquid often used as a fuel (3)
3. A vehicle used on farms (7)
4. Not right (9)
7. Reply (7)
10. Our star (3)

A single **CLYDESDALE HORSE** can pull a 100–200 kg carriage for **UP TO 8 HOURS A DAY!**

SUDOKUS

Solve the sudokus to hitch a free ride. Fill in the blank squares so that numbers 1 to 6 appear once in each row, column and 3 x 2 box.
See if you are right by flicking to page 96.

The first form of a horse-pulled carriage was a **ROMAN CHARIOT.** By the 15th century, horses were pulling **GRAND CARRIAGES** that could hold up to **8 PEOPLE.**

	4	5			1
	2			5	
					4
5		4		3	
3				4	2

Top puzzle:

		4	3	6	
	3				
		2	1		
		1	5		
				1	
	1	6	2		

Bottom puzzle:

4		6	1		
	3				6
			4		
		1			
5				3	
		3	5		4

Wordsearches

The Belgian Draft is on the lookout for its friends. Search left to right, up and down to find the words listed in the boxes below. See if you are right by flicking to page 96.

In the **19TH CENTURY, HORSES** and **PONIES** were used to **TRANSPORT COAL** along **MINE SHAFTS.**

w	p	o	l	o	e	g	l	m	g
b	o	z	t	r	g	k	a	p	e
s	u	f	f	o	l	k	p	t	z
f	r	e	i	b	e	r	g	e	r
i	r	i	s	h	s	p	o	r	t
b	a	b	s	f	a	r	m	n	p
i	c	o	h	u	n	t	i	n	g
m	i	n	i	n	g	o	t	k	a
h	n	b	r	e	t	o	n	g	o
v	g	z	e	z	q	i	v	z	c

breton

farm

freiberger

hunting

irish sport

mining

polo

racing

shire

suffolk

t m l n b b t c l d
r b l o d r p l j u
a f a l r a l y u t
n n b d e i o d t c
s f o e s d u e l h
p r u n s e g s a d
o u r b a d h d n r
r n t u g a i a d a
t e o r e z n l i f
l o g g i n g e t t

braided   labour
clydesdale   logging
dressage   oldenburg
dutch draft   ploughing
jutland   transport

BELGIAN DRAFT HORSES were bred by farmers in **BELGIUM** to work on farms. Today they still work on farms, although their strong build makes them suitable for **FORESTRY WORK.** They can pull up to **3,600 kg!**

SPOT THE DIFFERENCE

Compare the two images of agricultural horses.
Can you spot the five differences between the images?
See if you are right by flicking to page 97.

FARMERS all around the **WORLD** use **HORSES** to help them on their farms. They can help move large groups of cattle or sheep, or **PULL PLOUGHS** and **CARTS.**

MAZES

Lead the rider through the maze. Work your way around the maze until you reach the exit. See if you are right by flicking to page 97.

In show jumping, A HORSE and RIDER TRY TO CLEAR JUMPS as QUICKLY and CLEANLY as possible.

POLO is a team sport **PLAYED ON HORSEBACK. It is** one of the **OLDEST** known **TEAM SPORTS.**

GUESS WHAT?

Can you guess the answers to the horse questions below?
Check your guesses by flicking to page 97.

1. Police officers that ride horses are called:
   a) Mounted police
   b) Elevated police
   c) Knight police

2. Equestrian sport first appeared at which Summer Olympics?
   a) 1896 Athens
   b) 1900 Paris
   c) 1904 St Louis

3. The drink made from Russian heavy draft horses' milk is called:
   a) Kumis
   b) Sake
   c) Ouzo

4. Clydesdale horses stand at:
   a) 12–14 hands
   b) 14–16 hands
   c) 16–18 hands

5. Standardbred horses are the fastest horse at:
   a) Galloping
   b) Trotting
   c) Running

6. Large horses that are bred to work on farms are known as '____ horses':
   a) Draft
   b) Field
   c) Haulage

7. Show jumpers use this horse because of its great jumping skill:
   a) Shire
   b) Belgian
   c) Oldenburg

8. Belgian draft horses can pull up to:
   a) 3,600 kg
   b) 2,700 kg
   c) 450 kg

9. Thoroughbred horses are most commonly used in:
   a) Agriculture
   b) Mining
   c) Racing

10. In competitive races, horses can run at speeds of up to:
    a) 38 mph
    b) 43 mph
    c) 56 mph

WORD JUMBLES

The Russian heavy draft needs help to rearrange the jumbled letters to form horse-related words. See if you are right by flicking to page 97.

S D E R S E G A

N A I G R C

U J H P G W S O N I M

L A E S D C E L D Y

L O O P

DRESSAGE is a sport where a **HORSE** and **RIDER** score points for performing a routine. Points are awarded for factors including **OBEDIENCE, FLEXIBILITY** and **BALANCE.**

RUSSIAN HEAVY DRAFT HORSES were first officially registered in **1952,** and bred in the **SOVIET UNION.** They were used in agriculture, and their **MILK WAS FERMENTED** and made into a **DRINK** called 'KUMIS'.

Essential equipment and fabulous food

Discover fun facts and puzzles on horse food and equipment in this chapter.

HORSES love eating **APPLES** as **TREATS** but **LOVE BANANAS TOO!**

CROSSWORDS

Crack the crosswords by solving the cryptic clues below.
Answers have the same amount of letters as the number in brackets.
Can you work out the horse food and equipment keyword
using the letters in the shaded squares?
See if you are right by flicking to page 98.

The **RIDING BOOT** comes high enough up the leg to prevent **PINCHING** from the saddle, has a sturdy toe to **PROTECT THE RIDER** when on the ground, and has a heel to prevent the **FOOT** from sliding through the **STIRRUP.**

Across

1   Sledge (8)
5   Opposite of south (5)
7   Book of maps (5)
8   Stringed musical instrument (5)
9   Ascend (5)
10 Language spoken in Tokyo (8)

Down

1   Octopus part (8)
2   A city in Spain (9)
3   Say sorry (9)
4   Capable of happening (8)
6   Chaos (5)

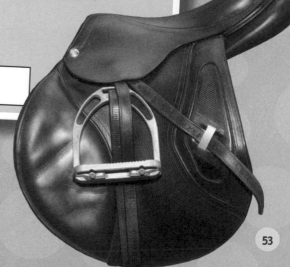

TWO of the SADDLE types for horse riding are the ENGLISH SADDLE and the WESTERN SADDLE. The English saddle has LESS LEATHER and is LIGHTER than the Western saddle. The Western saddle has a HORN ON THE FRONT, used for tying ROPE AROUND.

Across

4 Vegetable used to make chips (6)
6 Eat like a bird (4)
7 Use needles to make clothes out of wool (4)
8 Egg-shaped (4)
9 Owns; possesses (3)
10 Nothing (4)
11 Plant with stinging hairs (6)

Down

1 Offer to do something (9)
2 A 26-mile race (8)
3 Shape with four straight sides (9)
5 Facing something (8)

SUDOKUS

Solve the sudokus. Fill in the blank squares so that numbers 1 to 6 appear once in each row, column and 3 x 2 box. See if you are right by flicking to page 98.

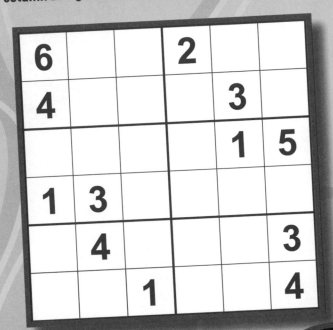

REINS are long, THIN STRAPS of material that are used by the rider to DIRECT the HORSE.

Puzzle 1

	3		5		
					3
	4		1		5
3		1		4	
2					
		5		2	

Puzzle 2

			6		5
					4
	3	5	4		
		1	3	5	
1					
2		3			

JODHPURS are TROUSERS worn whilst HORSE RIDING. They are tight-fitting and have STRONG PATCHES on the inside of the LEG.

Wordsearches

Search left to right, up and down to find the words listed in the boxes below.
See if you are right by flicking to page 98.

u	t	j	y	p	k	s	p	n	p
n	h	e	l	m	e	t	r	b	o
n	y	l	y	w	g	a	h	m	r
a	l	h	g	a	w	b	o	a	r
a	s	a	l	t	b	l	o	c	k
q	b	l	o	e	r	e	f	x	b
m	q	t	v	r	i	x	p	m	f
g	s	e	e	a	d	b	i	t	o
n	v	r	s	v	l	s	c	y	p
s	a	p	p	l	e	s	k	j	e

When riding a **HORSE** you should wear a **HELMET** to protect your **HEAD** in case you **FALL OFF**.

apples	helmet
bit	hoof pick
bridle	salt block
gloves	stable
halter	water

x	a	h	r	a	h	s	o	x	r
i	c	a	r	r	o	t	s	e	f
p	h	y	p	h	r	i	e	r	r
x	q	p	r	w	s	r	r	n	a
s	a	d	d	l	e	r	e	i	n
u	e	z	e	a	s	u	s	r	e
e	c	j	o	d	h	p	u	r	s
m	a	n	e	c	o	m	b	t	o
t	h	a	r	n	e	s	s	s	t
e	h	a	c	k	a	m	o	r	e

carrots

hackamore

harness

hay

horseshoe

jodhpurs

mane comb

rein

saddle

stirrup

NO MATTER the weather, **HORSE RIDERS** should **WEAR GLOVES.** This protects their **HANDS** and gives them **BETTER GRIP** on the **REINS.**

CLOSE UP

Match the mind-boggling magnifications to the named pictures opposite. See if you are right by flicking to page 99.

1

2

3

4

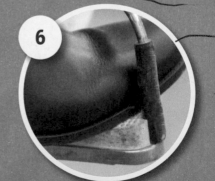

5

6

Water

1

Stirrup

2

Stable

3

Hoof pick

4

Bridle

5

Food concentrates

6

MAZES

Lead the horse to its favourite treat. Work your way around the maze until you reach the exit. See if you are right by flicking to page 99.

HORSES **LOVE** vegetable treats. **CARROTS** are one of their **FAVOURITES** and are extremely **GOOD FOR THEM.**

APPLES are good **SWEET TREATS** for horses as they are a healthier alternative to **SUGAR CUBES.**

GUESS WHAT?

Can you guess the answers to the horse food and equipment questions below?
Check your guesses by flicking to page 99.

1. The collective name for horse equipment is:
   a) Accessories
   b) Tack
   c) Attachments

2. Horses should not eat:
   a) Garden clippings
   b) Apples
   c) Dried grass

3. Which piece of horse equipment is given to married couples for good luck?
   a) Stirrup
   b) Bit
   c) Horseshoe

4. Horse riders use reins to:
   a) Direct the horse
   b) Get on the horse
   c) Clean the horse

5. Horses need 25–50 grams of what a day?
   a) Water
   b) Salt
   c) Grass

6. You can give these to horses for a treat:
   a) Rolos
   b) Meat bones
   c) Carrots

7. Horses are:
   a) Omnivores
   b) Herbivores
   c) Carnivores

8. Riders wear gloves to:
   a) Protect their hands
   b) Grip the reins
   c) Both

9. Horses sleep in a:
   a) Stable
   b) Sty
   c) Kennel

10. The average horse will eat this much hay a day:
   a) 3–5 kg
   b) 5–6 kg
   c) 7–10 kg

HORSESHOES protect a **HORSE'S HOOVES** from **DAMAGE.**

WORD JUMBLES

Rearrange the jumbled letters to form horse-related words.
See if you are right by flicking to page 99.

R H O E H S O S E

S J U P H D O R

R A C T O R

U S P I T R R

L A T E S B

When no fresh **GRASS** is available, horses must eat hay. The average **500 kg** horse will eat **7–10 kg** of hay a **DAY!**

GROOMING is an important part of **HORSE CARE.** It not only builds a relationship between the **HORSE** and **CARER,** but lets the carer check the **HORSE'S HEALTH.**

Majestic mythical horses

You won't believe your eyes when you see these fun facts and puzzles on mythical horses.

UNICORNS are mythical horses depicted as being **BEAUTIFUL** and with a **SINGLE HORN**. According to **MYTHS,** if a person touches a **PURE WHITE UNICORN,** they will find **JOY** and **HAPPINESS** for their **ENTIRE LIFE.**

CROSSWORDS

Help the centaur crack the crosswords by solving the cryptic clues below.
Answers have the same amount of letters as the number in brackets.
Can you work out the mythical horse keyword using the letters in the shaded squares?
See if you are right by flicking to page 100.

CENTAURS are creatures from **GREEK MYTHOLOGY** that have the **UPPER** body of a person and the **LOWER** body and **LEGS** of a **HORSE.**

Across

4 Get bigger (6)
6 Jealousy (4)
7 Tiny insect (4)
8 Object worn on a finger (4)
9 Fish-eating animal with flippers (4)
10 You might get a chocolate egg at this time of year (6)

Down

1 Very good (9)
2 Worth a lot of money (8)
3 Nine plus eight (9)
5 Become less (8)

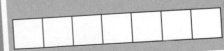

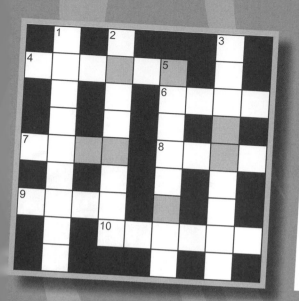

Across

4	Go back (6)
6	Solely; merely (4)
7	Someone you look up to (4)
8	Something you wear on your foot (4)
9	Border (4)
10	Save from danger (6)

Down

1	Day before Thursday (9)
2	Purchaser (8)
3	Very tasty (9)
5	Rubbish (8)

ARION is an immortal, **VERY FAST HORSE** bred by the **GREEK GODS.** It is also said that they gave this horse the **POWER OF SPEECH.**

SUDOKUS

Solve the sudokus with Pegasus. Fill in the blank squares so that numbers 1 to 6 appear once in each row, column and 3 x 2 box.
See if you are right by flicking to page 100.

				4	6
	6		2		
	5		4		
		2		1	
		1		3	
4	3				

PEGASUS is a male, flying, **PURE WHITE HORSE** from Greek mythology. One story says he was born after **PERSEUS**, a Greek hero, cut off the **HEAD OF MEDUSA** and **PEGASUS SPRANG** from her **NECK.**

68

A **CHOLLIMA** is a mythical **WINGED HORSE** that comes from **ASIAN MYTHOLOGY.** This winged horse is said to be too fast and refined to be ridden by **MORTAL PEOPLE.**

Wordsearches

Search left to right, up and down to find the
mythical horse and pony words listed in the boxes below.
See if you are right by flicking to page 100.

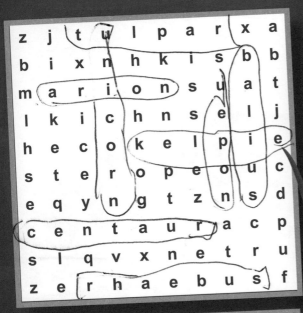

z	j	t	u	l	p	a	r	x	a
b	i	x	n	h	k	i	s	b	b
m	a	r	i	o	n	s	u	a	t
l	k	i	c	h	n	s	e	l	j
h	e	c	o	k	e	l	p	i	e
s	t	e	r	o	p	e	o	u	c
e	q	y	n	g	t	z	n	s	d
c	e	n	t	a	u	r	a	c	p
s	l	q	v	x	n	e	t	r	u
z	e	r	h	a	e	b	u	s	f

Not only is
POSEIDON GOD
of the sea in **GREEK
MYTHOLOGY,**
he is also the
GOD OF HORSES.

arion ✓
balius ✓
centaur ✓
epona ✓
kelpie ✓

neptune
rhaebus ✓
sterope
tulpar ✓
unicorn ✓

c	p	h	e	n	g	r	o	e	n
n	e	p	t	l	r	b	i	x	c
o	g	i	h	l	i	p	z	a	h
l	a	a	e	a	n	o	r	n	b
l	s	a	s	m	g	s	a	t	q
i	u	y	t	r	o	e	t	h	r
m	s	s	r	e	l	i	r	o	e
a	s	u	a	i	e	d	s	s	r
u	g	u	l	l	t	o	p	p	r
r	s	l	e	i	p	n	i	r	t

chollima	pegasus
gringolet	poseidon
gulltoppr	sleipnir
hengroen	thestral
llamrei	xanthos

NEPTUNE is the **ROMAN GOD OF THE SEA.** He is also associated with the sport of **HORSE RACING,** as he was often depicted **CROSSING THE SEA** in a **CHARIOT** pulled **BY HORSES.**

SPOT THE DIFFERENCE

Compare the two images of the unicorn.
Can you spot the five differences between the images?
See if you are right by flicking to page 101.

See if you are right by flicking to page 101.

The **NATIONAL ANIMAL** of SCOTLAND is the **UNICORN!**

MAZES

Lead the thestral through the maze. Work your way around the maze until you reach the exit. See if you are right by flicking to page 101.

FALKIRK, Scotland, is home to **THE KELPIES,** the **LARGEST** horse **SCULPTURE** in the **WORLD.**

THESTRALS are fictional horses from the **HARRY POTTER** universe created by J.K. Rowling. They have a **SKELETAL BODY, BAT-LIKE WINGS,** and a **REPTILIAN FACE.**

GUESS WHAT?

Can you guess the answers to the mythical horse questions below?
Check your guesses by flicking to page 101.

1. The god of horses in Greek mythology is:
   a) Poseidon
   b) Zeus
   c) Hades

2. Hippocampus had the lower body of which animal?
   a) Kangaroo
   b) Toad
   c) Fish

3. Kelpies often take the shape of horses and which other creature?
   a) Humans
   b) Lions
   c) Whales

4. Which mythical horse could speak?
   a) Unicorn
   b) Tulpar
   c) Arion

5. Thestrals' tail hair can be used for:
   a) Wand cores
   b) Potions
   c) Dental floss

6. King Arthur's horse was called:
   a) Hercules
   b) Hengroen
   c) Harold

7. Centaurs are the symbol of which sign of the zodiac?
   a) Cancer
   b) Sagittarius
   c) Aquarius

8. Sleipnir had how many legs?
   a) 4
   b) 8
   c) 12

9. In Greek myths, Pegasus brought this to Zeus, king of all gods:
   a) Thunder and lightning
   b) Snow and hail
   c) Clouds and rain

10. The unicorn is the national animal of which British country?
    a) England
    b) Wales
    c) Scotland

WORD JUMBLES

Epona needs help to rearrange the jumbled letters to form mythical horse-related words. See if you are right by flicking to page 101.

U S S P A G E

A E C R N U T

I R A N O

U T L A P R

I U N C O N R

EPONA was the **CELTIC GODDESS OF HORSES.** It is said that when she **TRAVELLED ON HORSEBACK** it was **IMPOSSIBLE TO CATCH HER.**

TULPAR is the name used in Asian Turkic languages to refer to a **WINGED HORSE.** It is the **STATE EMBLEM** of **KAZAKHSTAN** and **MONGOLIA.**

Horses in history

Horses have played a part in human life for centuries. Find out more about horses in history in this chapter.

Many seats on **CAROUSELS** are shaped like horses. They MOVE UP AND DOWN as if they are **GALLOPING** along to **MUSIC.**

CROSSWORDS

Crack the crosswords by solving the cryptic clues below.
Answers have the same amount of letters as the number in brackets.
Can you work out the keyword using the letters in the shaded squares?
See if you are right by flicking to page 102.

Across

4 Urge on (9)
6 Opposite of no (3)
8 Unit of length (5)
9 See-through (5)
10 Crafty and cunning (3)
12 Change into something else (9)

Down

1 Leg joint (4)
2 Give a brief statement of (9)
3 Prickly desert plant (6)
5 All (5)
6 Type of sailing boat (5)
7 Playground item that moves up and down (3-3)
11 Songbird (4)

The **TROJAN HORSE** is a **LARGE WOODEN HORSE** from the **TROJAN WAR** waged against the city of **TROY.**

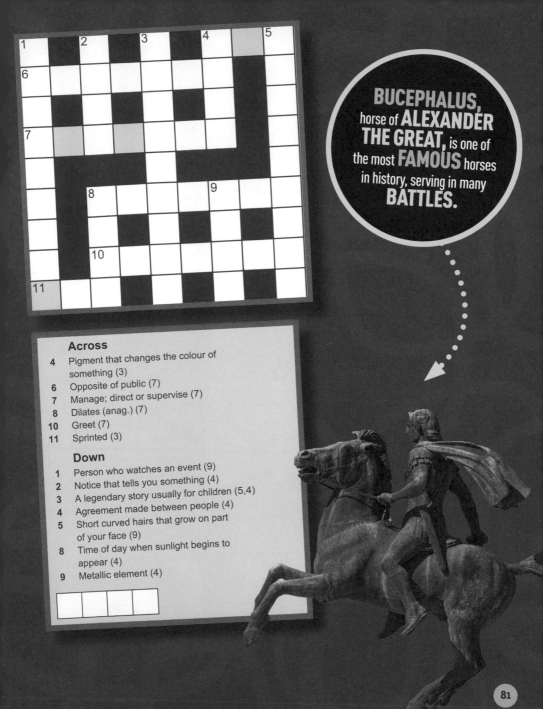

BUCEPHALUS, horse of ALEXANDER THE GREAT, is one of the most FAMOUS horses in history, serving in many BATTLES.

Across
4 Pigment that changes the colour of something (3)
6 Opposite of public (7)
7 Manage; direct or supervise (7)
8 Dilates (anag.) (7)
10 Greet (7)
11 Sprinted (3)

Down
1 Person who watches an event (9)
2 Notice that tells you something (4)
3 A legendary story usually for children (5,4)
4 Agreement made between people (4)
5 Short curved hairs that grow on part of your face (9)
8 Time of day when sunlight begins to appear (4)
9 Metallic element (4)

SUDOKUS

Solve the sudokus with Marengo and Copenhagen.
Fill in the blank squares so that numbers 1 to 6 appear once in each row,
column and 3 x 2 box. See if you are right by flicking to page 102.

		5			
6		2			
	5		1		3
3		4		6	
			6		1
			3		

MARENGO was the horse of **NAPOLEON I** of **FRANCE**. He was named after the **BATTLE OF MARENGO,** in which he guided his rider to **SAFETY.**

				3	
6				5	4
2			4		
		4			6
5	4				1
	2				

			3		
		1		4	6
6	1				
				5	1
1	5		4		
		4			

Wordsearches

Start the search for historical horse terms. Search left to right, up and down to find the words listed in the boxes below. See if you are right by flicking to page 102.

d	w	e	l	l	i	n	g	t	o	n	a
c	h	u	x	h	n	o	r	h	i	t	o
a	o	n	a	p	o	l	e	o	n	r	b
v	r	t	a	r	l	k	j	l	k	o	a
a	s	x	r	s	t	i	a	x	e	j	t
l	e	m	a	r	e	n	g	o	t	a	t
r	b	l	u	r	u	g	h	w	z	n	l
y	c	o	p	e	n	h	a	g	e	n	e
e	a	u	e	d	d	o	r	v	m	p	a
l	n	v	l	i	e	r	s	z	a	l	u
f	h	w	o	s	x	s	e	o	d	a	g
b	u	c	e	p	h	a	l	u	s	y	h

A **HOBBY HORSE** is a **CHILD'S TOY** made of a **POLE** and **WOODEN HORSE'S HEAD.** It was very popular in the **OLDEN DAYS** before **CARS.**

Bucephalus
battle
cavalry
Copenhagen

Marengo
Napoleon
Trojan
Wellington

r e d h r v h e a l c r
s t e e d i a u r s a o
o k o r o c w v h t r c
z s b s m t h r o m o k
r v b e m o o k r a u i
h i s t o r y a s n s n
h r h l h i s t e p e g
w s o y h a e k w i l t
b z r m o n m t e t o a
a f a i r g r o u n d i
p e r f o r m a n c e l
h o z s c s t a t u e s

carousel
fairground
history
performance

rocking
statue
steed
Victorian

A **ROCKING HORSE** is a child's toy of a **WOODEN HORSE** mounted on rockers. **QUEEN VICTORIA** liked rocking horses and her love for them increased their **POPULARITY** and **PRODUCTION.**

SPOT THE DIFFERENCE

Compare the two images of the carousel.
Can you spot the five differences between the images?
See if you are right by flicking to page 103.

MAZES

Lead Clever Hans through the maze. Work your way around the maze until you reach the exit. See if you are right by flicking to page 103.

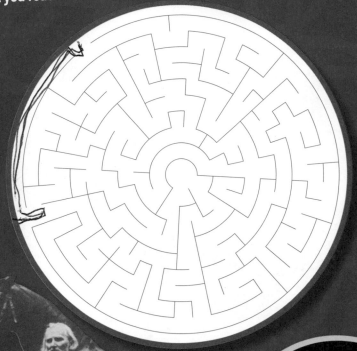

CLEVER HANS

was a horse who lived in **GERMANY.** It was believed he could do **ARITHMETIC,** however, it turns out he was picking up on **SIGNALS** from humans that guided him to the correct answer rather than solving problems himself.

1	2	3	4	5	6
7	8	9	10	11	12
13	14	15	16	17
18	19	20	21	22
23	24	25	26	27

A

G

N P Q

T U V W X Y Z

28 29 30 0

M'KINLEY

ROOSEVELT

365 366

GUESS WHAT?

Can you guess the answers to the questions below?
Check your guesses by flicking to page 103.

1. Clever Hans came from:
   a) France
   b) Germany
   c) Poland

2. The Duke of Wellington's horse shared its name with the capital city of which country?
   a) Denmark
   b) Sweden
   c) Italy

3. Which historical figure had a horse named Marengo?
   a) Genghis Khan
   b) Napoleon I
   c) Alexander the Great

4. What material were carousel horses traditonally made from?
   a) Plastic
   b) Wood
   c) Rubber

5. Which ancient city was the Trojan horse brought into?
   a) Rome
   b) Athens
   c) Troy

6. Which century did Beautiful Jim Key perform in?
   a) 20th
   b) 18th
   c) 16th

7. The oldest carousel can be found in which country?
   a) Italy
   b) Germany
   c) Great Britain

8. Which queen's love for rocking horses increased their popularity?
   a) Elizabeth
   b) Victoria
   c) Margaret

9. Trigger was famous in the 1940s and 50s for:
   a) Horse racing
   b) Starring in films
   c) Doing arithmetic

10. A hobby horse is not just a toy, it is also used in:
   a) Salsa dancing
   b) Highland dancing
   c) Morris dancing

WORD JUMBLES

Rearrange the jumbled letters to form horse-related words.
See if you are right by flicking to page 103.

J O R T N A

O R C A S U L E

B T T E A L

O R P E F A R M N C E

R G O K I N C

TRIGGER was a palomino stallion who STARRED in WESTERN FILMS with his owner ROY ROGERS. You can find Trigger's HOOFPRINTS outside Grauman's Chinese Theatre in HOLLYWOOD.

TO SID MANY-HAPPY-TRAILS
Roy Rogers & TRIGGER
APRIL-21-1949

Solutions

Crosswords

Crossword 1:

I	N	V	I	S	I	B	L	E	
M		I		U		X		T	
P	I	E		L		M		T	
O		W	H	I	S	P	E	R	
R			A			E		E	
T	O	W	A	R	D	S		M	
A		A		S		O	N	E	
N		R			F			L	
T	E	M	P	O	R	A	R	Y	

Keyword: ANDALUSIAN

Crossword 2:

N	O	D				H		C
I			I	M	A	G	I	N	E
G	A	S		I		B		N
H		H	A	R	V	E	S	T
T		O			R		I
M	E	N	T	I	O	N		P
A		E		C		A	G	E
R	E	S	P	E	C	T		D
E		T			E	Y	E

Keyword: ARABIAN

Sudokus

Sudoku 1:

6	1	4	2	3	5
3	2	5	1	4	6
1	5	3	6	2	4
4	6	2	5	1	3
5	4	1	3	6	2
2	3	6	4	5	1

Sudoku 2:

3	5	2	1	4	6
1	6	4	2	3	5
6	2	3	4	5	1
5	4	1	6	2	3
2	3	6	5	1	4
4	1	5	3	6	2

Sudoku 3:

5	1	6	3	2	4
3	4	2	6	5	1
2	6	3	1	4	5
4	5	1	2	3	6
1	3	4	5	6	2
6	2	5	4	1	3

Wordsearches

Wordsearch 1:

h	m	u	s	t	a	n	g	l	o
o	a	a	y	c	s	t	y	f	u
r	i	f	t	o	t	r	r	r	j
s	i	c	e	l	a	n	d	i	c
e	q	a	t	t	l	t	a	e	v
e	a	p	p	a	l	o	o	s	a
y	g	e	l	d	i	n	g	i	p
e	i	r	k	d	o	f	o	a	l
s	e	q	u	i	n	e	x	n	p
m	n	d	s	g	e	a	r	u	r

Wordsearch 2:

a	n	d	a	l	u	s	i	a	n
p	g	p	p	g	b	o	i	n	r
x	f	e	m	a	r	e	w	f	a
t	d	r	m	l	t	d	a	i	n
x	l	c	a	l	r	l	w	l	e
n	t	h	n	o	t	e	d	l	x
s	l	e	e	p	i	n	g	y	y
e	a	r	a	b	i	a	n	n	o
r	t	o	l	f	e	t	a	n	o
h	a	n	o	v	e	r	i	a	n

Close up

Page 14–15

1–4 Percheron

2–6 Arabian

3–2 American Paint horse

4–1 Norwegian Fjord horse

5–3 Icelandic horse

6–5 Friesian

Mazes

Page 16–17

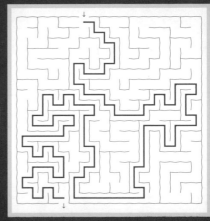

Guess what?

Page 18–19

1. b) Hands

2. a) Arabian

3. c) Foal

4. a) 205

5. c) Eyes

6. b) Spotted

7. c) 19 hands

8. a) 21 seconds

9. b) Vomit

10. a) American Paint horse

Word jumbles

FILLY

PERCHERON

MUSTANG

ARABIAN

HANOVERIAN

Solutions

Crossword

Page 22-23

Crossword 1

```
F O R B I D D E N
A . O . . . A . E
N A P . C . M . C
T . E X A M P L E
A . . R . . L . S
S E R I O U S . S
T . I . L . P E A
I . P . . . O . R
C H E M I S T R Y
```

Keyword: EXMOOR

Crossword 2

```
D I S T A N T . W
I . . R . H . . O
R . C . C L E A N
E . E . H . P . D
C A R N I V O R E
T . T . T . O . R
I M A G E . H . F
O . I . . . C . U
N . N A T U R A L
```

Keyword: HIGHLAND

Sudokus

Page 24-25

```
2 6 1 5 3 4
4 5 3 6 2 1
3 4 6 1 5 2
5 1 2 4 6 3
6 3 4 2 1 5
1 2 5 3 4 6
```

```
5 1 4 6 2 3
2 6 3 1 4 5
4 3 5 2 6 1
6 2 1 5 3 4
3 5 2 4 1 6
1 4 6 3 5 2
```

```
4 5 6 2 3 1
1 2 3 5 6 4
5 3 4 6 1 2
2 6 1 3 4 5
6 4 2 1 5 3
3 1 5 4 2 6
```

Wordsearches

Page 26-27

```
w e l s h j h o o f
a s s a t e a g u e
k q a n u a f r k p
e w m d z s l e e g
r i q a t t i x r r
i t n l r u n m r p
s h y w t r g o y k
k e g o n c e o b p
a r a o r o r r o p
y s o d f n b h g o
```

```
c o n n e m a r a s
b o s n i a n h s n
g k k a m r d i h e
o m r j v k a g e w
t r o t e i r h t f
l u s z f n t l l o
a k j b p g m a a r
n o y j u s o n n e
d u l m e n o d d s
k s i n u v r v k t
```

Solutions

Crosswords

Grid 1:
O	B	V	I	O	U	S		Y
T			U		U	S	E	E
H	A	M	S	T	E	R		S
E		O			F			T
R		R	U	M	B	A		E
W		N			C			R
I		I	N	S	T	E	A	D
S	O	N		E				A
E		G	R	A	V	I	T	Y

Keyword: MINING

Grid 2:
A	I	R	P	O	R	T		I
R				I		R	U	N
G	O	R	I	L	L	A		C
E		E			C			O
N		S	P	O	R	T		R
T		P			O			R
I		O	B	S	E	R	V	E
N	U	N		U				C
A		D	E	N	T	I	S	T

Keyword: RACING

Sudokus

Sudoku 1:
2	4	5	3	6	1
1	3	6	2	4	5
6	2	3	5	1	4
5	1	4	6	3	2
4	6	2	1	5	3
3	5	1	4	2	6

Sudoku 2:
1	2	4	3	6	5
6	3	5	4	2	1
5	4	2	1	3	6
3	6	1	5	4	2
2	5	3	6	1	4
4	1	6	2	5	3

Sudoku 3:
4	2	6	1	5	3
1	3	5	2	4	6
3	5	2	4	6	1
6	4	1	3	2	5
5	1	4	6	3	2
2	6	3	5	1	4

Wordsearches

Wordsearch 1:
```
w p o l o e g l m g
b o z t r g k a p e
s u f f o l k p t z
f r e i b e r g e r
i r i s h s p o r t
b a b s f a r m n p
i c o h u n t i n g
m i n i n g o t k a
h n b r e t o n g o
v g z e z q i v z c
```

Wordsearch 2:
```
t m l n b b t c l d
r b l o d r p l j u
a f a l r a l y t t
n n b d e i o d u c
s f o e s d u e l h
p r u n s e g s l d
o u r b a d h d a r
r n t u g a i a d a
t e o r e z n l l f
l o g g i n g e t t
```

96

Page 44-45 — Spot the difference

Page 46-47 — Mazes

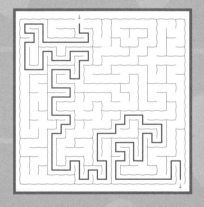

Page 48-49 — Guess what?

1. a) Mounted police
2. b) 1900 Paris
3. a) Kumis
4. c) 16–18 hands
5. b) Trotting
6. a) Draft
7. c) Oldenburg
8. a) 3,600 kg
9. c) Racing
10. b) 43 mph

Word jumbles

DRESSAGE

RACING

SHOW JUMPING

CLYDESDALE

POLO

Solutions

Crosswords

Page 52–53

Crossword 1:

T	O	B	O	G	G	A	N
E		A			P		P
N	O	R	T	H	O		O
	C		A	T	L	A	S
	E		V	O		G	S	I
C	E	L	L	O		G		S	I
L		O		C	L	I	M	B
E		N				S		L
	J	A	P	A	N	E	S	E

Keyword: HELMET

Crossword 2:

	V		M				R
P	O	T	A	T	O		E
	L		R		P	E	C	K
	U		A		P		T
K	N	I	T		O	V	A	L
	T		H	A	S		N
Z	E	R	O		I		G
	E		N	E	T	T	L	E
	R			E		E	E

Keyword: STIRRUP

Sudokus

Page 54–55

6	5	3	2	4	1
4	1	2	5	3	6
2	6	4	3	1	5
1	3	5	4	6	2
5	4	6	1	2	3
3	2	1	6	5	4

1	3	4	5	6	2
5	2	6	4	1	3
6	4	2	1	3	5
3	5	1	2	4	6
2	1	3	6	5	4
4	6	5	3	2	1

3	1	4	6	2	5
5	6	2	1	3	4
6	3	5	4	1	2
4	2	1	3	5	6
1	5	6	2	4	3
2	4	3	5	6	1

Wordsearches

Page 56–57

u	t	j	y	p	k	s	p	n	p
n	h	e	l	m	e	t	r	b	o
n	y	l	y	w	g	a	h	m	r
a	l	h	g	a	w	b	o	a	r
a	s	a	l	t	b	l	o	c	k
q	b	l	o	e	r	e	f	x	b
m	q	t	v	r	i	x	p	m	f
g	s	e	e	a	d	b	i	t	o
n	v	r	s	v	l	s	c	y	p
s	a	p	p	l	e	s	k	j	e

x	a	h	r	a	h	s	o	x	r
i	c	a	r	r	o	t	s	e	f
p	h	y	p	h	r	i	e	r	r
x	q	p	r	w	s	r	r	n	a
s	a	d	d	l	e	r	e	i	n
u	e	z	e	a	s	u	s	r	e
e	c	j	o	d	h	p	u	r	s
m	a	n	e	c	o	m	b	t	o
t	h	a	r	n	e	s	s	s	t
e	h	a	c	k	a	m	o	r	e

Page 58–59

Close up

1–3 Stable

3–5 Bridle

5–4 Hoof pick

2–1 Water

4–6 Food concentrates

6–2 Stirrup

Page 60–61

Mazes

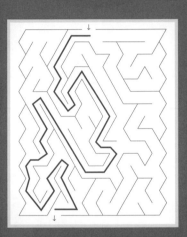

Page 62–63

Guess what?

1. b) Tack

2. a) Garden clippings

3. c) Horseshoe

4. a) Direct the horse

5. b) Salt

6. c) Carrots

7. b) Herbivores

8. c) Both

9. a) Stable

10. c) 7–10 kg

Word jumbles

HORSESHOE

JODHPURS

CARROT

STIRRUP

STABLE

Solutions

Page 66–67

Crosswords

		E		V			S	
E	X	P	A	N	D	E		
		C		L		E	N	V	Y
		E		U		C		E
F	L	E	A		R	I	N	G
		L		B		E		T
S	E	A	L		A		E
		N		E	A	S	T	E	R
		T				E	N

Keyword: PEGASUS

		W		C			D	
R	E	T	U	R	N		E	
		D		S		O	N	L	Y
		N		T		N		I
H	E	R	O		S	O	C	K
		S		M		E		I
E	D	G	E		N		O
		A		R	E	S	C	U	E
		Y				E	S

Keyword: UNICORN

Page 68–69

Sudokus

2	1	5	3	4	6
3	6	4	2	5	1
1	5	3	4	6	2
6	4	2	5	1	3
5	2	1	6	3	4
4	3	6	1	2	5

6	4	1	2	3	5
3	5	2	6	1	4
1	6	5	3	4	2
2	3	4	5	6	1
4	2	3	1	5	6
5	1	6	4	2	3

2	5	4	1	6	3
3	1	6	4	2	5
1	2	5	3	4	6
4	6	3	2	5	1
5	4	1	6	3	2
6	3	2	5	1	4

Page 70–71

Wordsearches

Page 72–73

Spot the difference

Page 74–75

Mazes

Page 76–77

Guess what?

1. a) Poseidon
2. c) Fish
3. a) Humans
4. c) Arion
5. a) Wand cores

6. b) Hengroen
7. b) Sagittarius
8. b) 8
9. a) Thunder and lightning
10. c) Scotland

Word jumbles

PEGASUS

CENTAUR

ARION

TULPAR

UNICORN

Solutions

Page 80–81

Crosswords

```
. K . S C . . . | S S . F . D Y E
E N C O U R A G E | P R I V A T E . Y
. E . M . C . V . | E . G . I . A . Y
Y E S . M E T R E | C O N T R O L . E
A . E . A . U . R | T . Y . . . . . L
C L E A R . S L Y | A . D E T A I L S
H . S . I . . A . | T . A . A . R . H
T R A N S F O R M | O . W E L C O M E
. W . E . K . . . | R A N . E . N . S
```

Keyword: CAROUSEL   Keyword: TROY

Page 82–83

Sudokus

1	4	5	2	3	6
6	3	2	4	1	5
2	5	6	1	4	3
3	1	4	5	6	2
4	2	3	6	5	1
5	6	1	3	2	4

4	5	1	6	3	2
6	3	2	1	5	4
2	6	5	4	1	3
3	1	4	5	2	6
5	4	3	2	6	1
1	2	6	3	4	5

5	4	6	3	1	2
2	3	1	5	4	6
6	1	5	2	3	4
4	2	3	6	5	1
1	5	2	4	6	3
3	6	4	1	2	5

Page 84–85

Wordsearches